Little Jack Horner

Illustrated by Laura Huliska-Beith

Designed by Jaime Lucero

ISBN: 978-0-545-26772-4

Copyright © 2010 by Scholastic Inc.

All rights reserved. Published by Scholastic Inc.

12 11 10 9 8 7 6 5 4 3 2 1   10 11 12 13 14 15/0

Little Jack Horner

sat in the corner

4 eating his Christmas pie.

He stuck in his thumb

and he pulled out a plum.

And he said...

"What a good boy am I!"